THE Glitter Stickers COLLECTION

DK

LONDON, NEW YORK, MUNICH,
MELBOURNE, and DELHI

WRITTEN AND EDITED BY Penny Arlon,
Lorrie Mack, Dawn Sirett and Jane Yorke
PHOTOGRAPHY BY Andy Crawford,
Dave King and Gary Ombler
JACKET DESIGN Anthony Limerick
and David McDonald
COVER EDITOR Julie Ferris
DTP DESIGNER David McDonald
PRODUCTION Vivianne Cracknell
PICTURE RESEARCHER Sarah Mills
PROJECT MANAGER Nigel Duffield

First American Edition, 2006

Published in the United States by
DK Publishing, Inc.
375 Hudson Street
New York, New York 10014

05 06 07 08 09 10 9 8 7 6 5 4 3 2 1

A Cataloging-in-Publication record for this book
is available from the Library of Congress.

ISBN 0-7566-2117-8

Color reproduction by
M.D.P., United Kingdom
Printed and bound in China by
L. Rex Printing Co. Ltd.

Discover more at
www.dk.com

Welcome to

In the first part of this book, you can learn how to make a dancing fairy card and a fairy angel. Dress up like a fairy with your own magic wand and glittering tiara, and create some beautiful butterflies to decorate your bedroom.

Then it's time for some sticker fun. Match the glittery stickers to the shapes. When you have completed all the pages in the book, you can use any leftover stickers to make your own pretty pictures!

Dancing fairy card

Send happy birthday greetings with a fairy ballerina in a frilly tutu!

Here's how to make it

1

From posterboard, cut and fold a blank card to the size and shape you want.

Now cut a strip of colored paper and fold it into an accordion shape that looks like this.

2

Open your card and sketch a fairy ballerina over the fold.

Spread glue thinly on one flat end of the accordion.

Press it down on the card here.

3

Spread glue thinly on the other end of the accordion in the same way.

4

Close the card, then press down gently on top, where the paper has been glued.

5

Leave the glue to dry for a few minutes, so when you open the card...

6

...the tutu pops out!

Sticker fun

Surround your fairy with stars and butterflies.

Fairy angels

Twinkle, twinkle little angels
Hanging on the Christmas tree.
Paper fairies bright with stickers
Wave their starry wands at me.

1 Cut out your shape

You'll need one paper plate for each angel. On the front, draw a pencil outline that looks like this, and cut along the lines.

2 Add sparkly details

Put your decorations on the other side of the plate.

Glitter

Sequins

3 Staple the skirt

You only need one staple here.

Sticker fun

Fairies look pretty in pink hearts and flowers.

Wands and tiaras
Magic up a fairy wand...
and wish for a glittering tiara

Magic wand

1 Cut out two star shapes from posterboard, using the star template on page 12. Cover them with foil.

2 Take a plant stick or a length of doweling 12 in (30 cm) long. Wind a strip of colored paper or ribbon around the stick and fix it with a dab of glue at each end.

3 Decorate one of your stars and and stick it to the other one, wrong sides together, with the stick fastened firmly between them.

Sticker fun

Use your favorite stickers to personalize your wand.

Fairy tiara

1 Cut a paper plate in half. Draw a zigzag around the edge—see the tiara template on page 12.

2 Carefully cut out the zigzag.

3 Place some stickers, sequins, or glitter on your tiara in the design of your choice.

4 Fix your decorations in place. Now cut a strip of posterboard that fits around your head and staple it to the tiara.

Enchanted butterflies

Amaze your friends by creating beautiful butterflies tha will perch on your finger, your straw, or the end of your pencil

Attach weight here.
Use glue to stick a small coin or washer to both wingtips.
PLACE THE FOLD IN THE TRACING PAPER HERE
1

Template

Use this template to make your butterfly.

* Fold a sheet of tracing paper in half and position the fold as indicated (left). Now draw around the dotted line.
* Cut out the wing shape and open out your butterfly.
* Lay the shape on a piece of posterboard and draw around it.

Cut out the butterfly shape from posterboard.

Wonderful wings

Use pictures of real butterflies for design inspiration, or create your own fantasy flutterers from your imagination.

Sticker fun
Make enchanting patterns on your butterfly wings with stickers.
2
3

Draw markings with black felt-tip pen and color in the spaces.

Glue on the coins or washers last.

Fairy templates

Use these fantastic fairy templates to help you create the ultimate fairy accessories.

For a crown-like tiara use this template.
You don't need a fairy godmother to make your wishes come true!

For a perfect pair of fairy wings, use this template, which is one side of a pair of wings.
Use this star-shaped template for the wishing wand.
For a dreamy tiara use this cloud shape.

Dress up for fairy fun!

Choose dresses for these three fairies to wear. Then, find the right wings for each fairy.

Which fairy do you like best?
fairy wings

This is Sunflower.

This is Snowdrop.

This is Rose.

What can the fairies wear on their heads?
Find five flowers for Sunflower.
Give Rose a red and pink hat.
Put ver garla drop.
Now make a necklace with some of you tery stickers.
Finally, find each fairy a magic wand.

Fairy wishes

Find the blue fairy who conjures up wishes from her magic chest.

Now let's decorate the chest with two glittery flower stickers.

cuddly kitten
silver tiara
pretty present
What special wishes have magically appeared?
birthday cake
bright balloons
shiny shoes
What would you wish for?
Make these pages sparkle with twinkly star stickers!

A secret garden

Can you find all the stickers to complete this secret fairy garden?

Look for a spotted bug.

Put three glittery fish stickers in the pond.

Add some red toadstools.

Find three fairy friends.

Look for five apples.
Now add two sparkly toadstool stickers.
Find six colored flowers and three glittery flower stick

A fairy tea party

A fairy has invited her friends for a tea-party picnic. Can you find her, then help her lay out the cups and saucers?

cup and saucer

cup and saucer

cup and saucer

teapot

cupcakes

Now let's find the teapot and a plate of delicious cupcakes.

We're all ready for some fairy fun!

A royal castle

et's put three princesses
n the castle windows.

Add a sparkly moon.

Princess

squeak!

Make the castle twinkle with glittery hearts and flowers.

Pri
Bella Blue

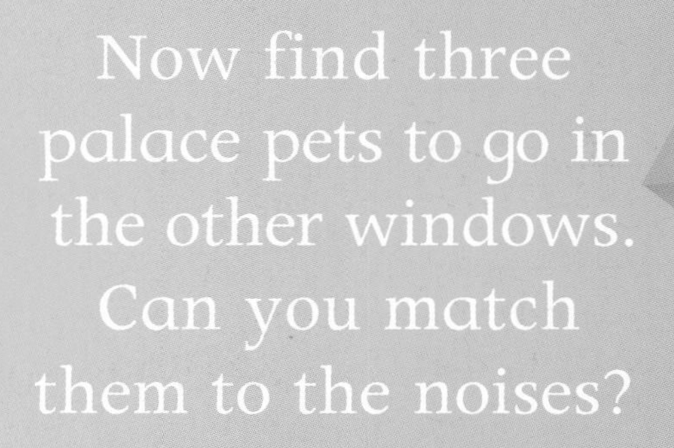

Now find three palace pets to go in the other windows. Can you match them to the noises?

meow!

Princess
Polly Pink

Finally, wave goodbye to everyone!

Dress up for the ball!

Help this princess get ready. First, find her tiara.

Where's he twinkly star wand?

sparkly blue

twinkly rec

fluffy pink

shiny silver

Now let's find all her shoes Which pair do you like best

Next put on her blue dress.

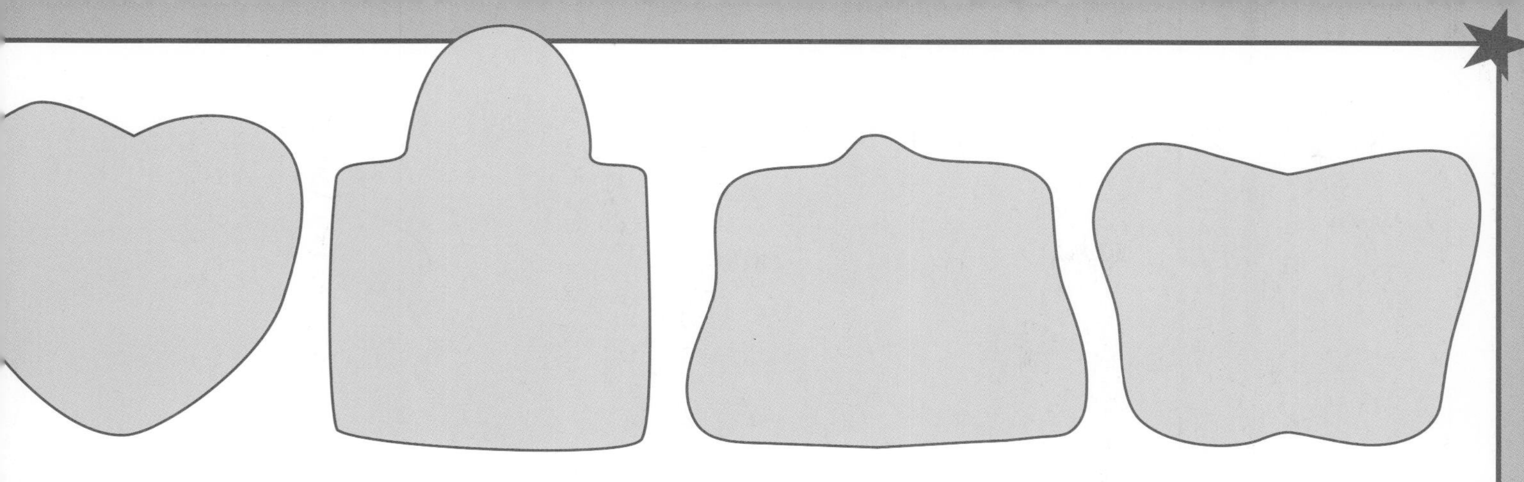

Where are the princess's party bags? Which is your favorite?

Finally, put her pink beads,
her heart ring, and her jeweled crown
into her jewelry box. Make the box twinkle with four
glittery flower stickers and one sparkly heart sticker!

At the dressing table

Who's the fairest of them all? Put a picture of a beautiful princess in the biggest mirror.

Now find all her things:
two perfume bottles,
a hairdryer, a hairbrush
a necklace, a barrette,
and a small makeup jar.

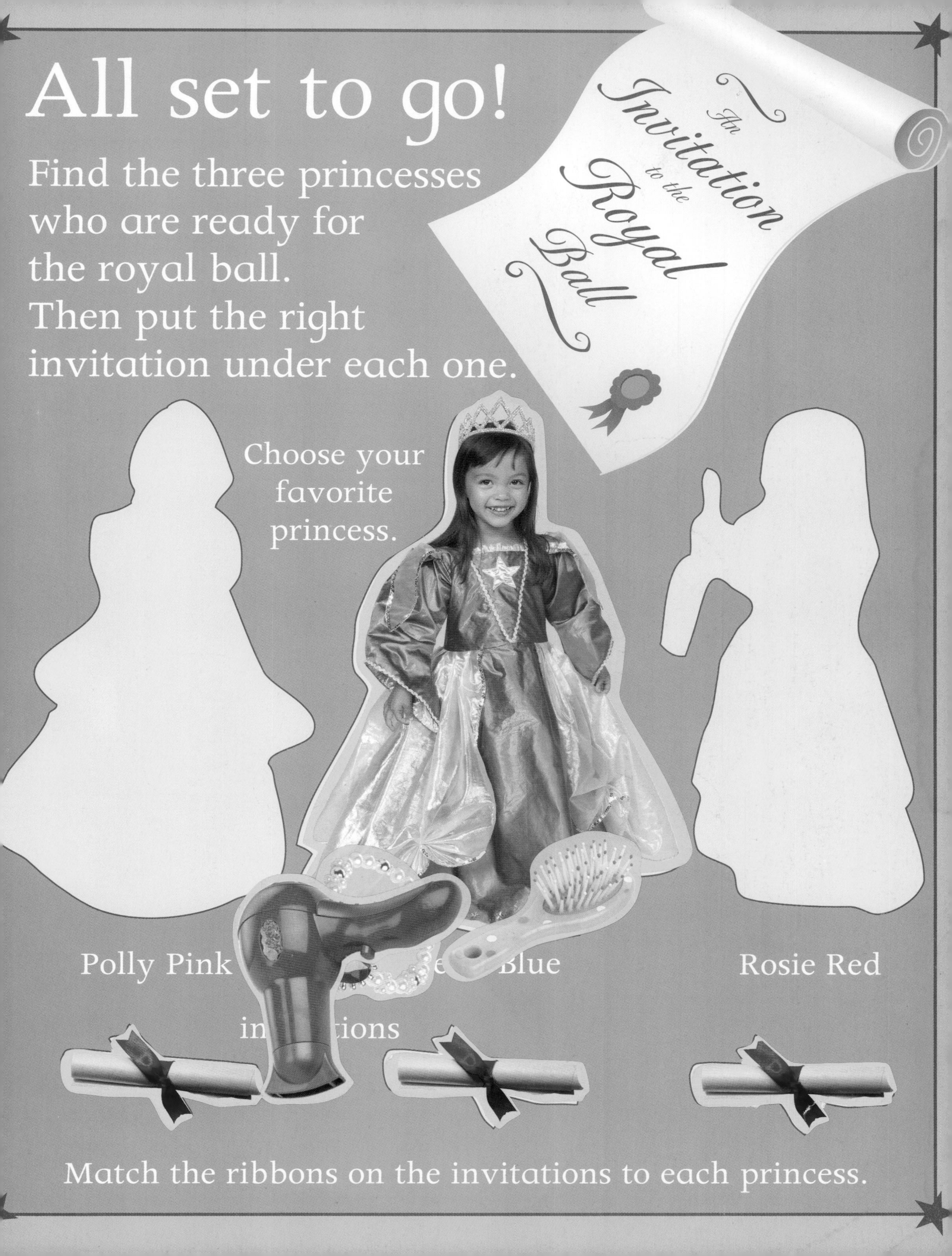

All set to go!

Find the three princesses who are ready for the royal ball. Then put the right invitation under each one.

Choose your favorite princess.

Match the ribbons on the invitations to each princess.

A princess carriage

Princess Bella Blue is going for a ride in her carriage. Can you find her?

Decorate the carriage with some glittery sticker shapes.

Now light up the night sky
with twinkly star stickers and
a sparkly moon sticker!
horses
Finally, put
pretty red and purple
bows on the horses.

Dressing up for ballet

Help these ballerinas find all their ballet things so they can start to dance.

Put two pink bows in this girl's hair.

Can you find this ballerina's pink starry wand?

Where's her pretty pink tutu?

Don't forget her pink satin ballet shoes!

Now she looks like a real ballerina.

Find one blue bow for
this girl's hair.

Put a
bouquet of
red roses in
her hand.

Look for
a beautiful
blue tutu for
this ballerina
to wear.

Now both
ballerinas are
ready to dance.
Which one do
you like best?

Find a
pair of blue
ballet shoes
to match
the tutu.

At the ballet class

Find four little girls practicing different ballet movements in their ballet class. Can you copy what each girl is doing?

Can you find Sarah? She is holding the bar and pointing her right foot

Where is Rebecca? She is holding her arms out and pointing her left foot to the side.

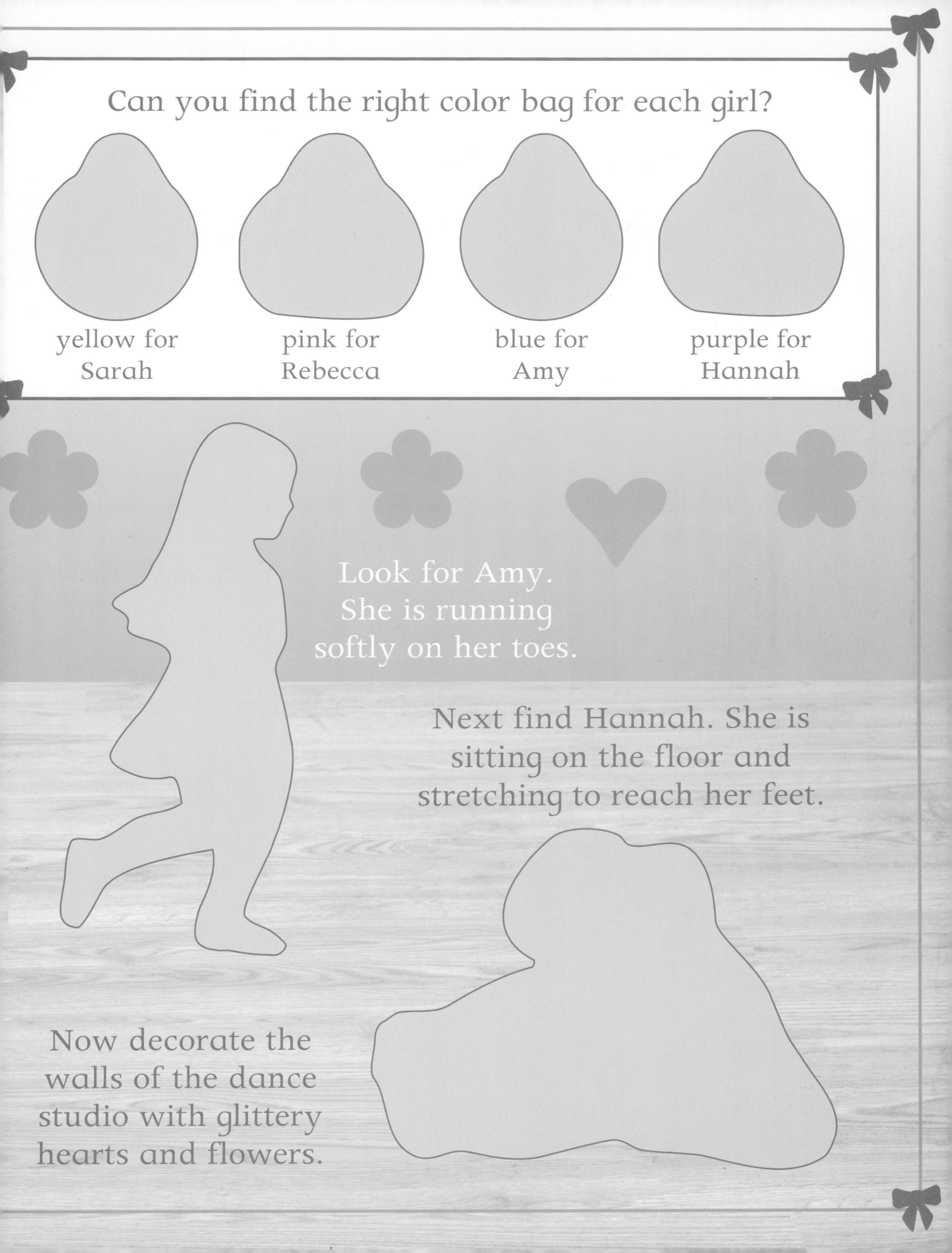

Can you find the right color bag for each girl?

yellow for Sarah

pink for Rebecca

blue for Amy

purple for Hannah

Look for Amy. She is running softly on her toes.

Next find Hannah. She is sitting on the floor and stretching to reach her feet.

Now decorate the walls of the dance studio with glittery hearts and flowers.

Show time!

How exciting! The four ballerinas are in a show. The curtains open and the performance begins.

Find Hannah, Sarah, and Rebecca. They are holding their arms out and daintily pointing one foot to the side.

Make the curtains sparkle with glittery hearts, flowers, and bows.

Look for Amy. Her arms are held gracefully above her head.

Imagine you are one of the ballerinas and pretend to dance in the show.

Now scatter ten
ed roses on the stage.

Dress up for magic fun!

Dress up the witch and wizard, then find all the magical things they need.

Put some glittery bat stickers in the sky.

Find the witch's dress and hat.

Where's her lucky black cat?

A witch needs a broomstick.

Find the wizard's pointy hat.
Put a spider on the web.
bracadabra! Make a wizard's and appear!
Fill the sky with twinkly star stickers.
ut sparkling stars and oons on the izard's cloak.
Put a stack of magic spellbooks here.
Do you see the wizard's slimy toad?

A haunted house

Finish this spooky page with your magical stickers!

Let's look for the flying wizard!

Who says meow?

meow!

Can you spot some spooky faces on these pages?

Beware of the
full moon!
hoo-
hoo!
Who says
hoo-hoo?
Who is riding on
this broomstick?
Finally, fill the night sky
with some glittery bat stickers and
lots of twinkling star stickers!

Hocus pocus!

Can you find the things that are going into this magic cauldron?

You need:
a snail, a bat,
a snake, a frog,
a spider, a worm,
a fly, a rat, and
two caterpillars.

Now make
the cauldron
sparkle with
glittery star
stickers!

Abracadabra!

Find the witch who has cast a spell. What exciting things has she conjured from her cauldron?

witch

gold coins

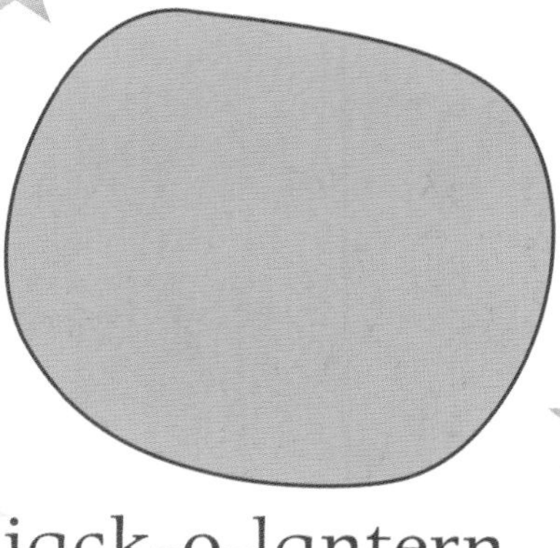

jack-o-lantern

lollipop

present

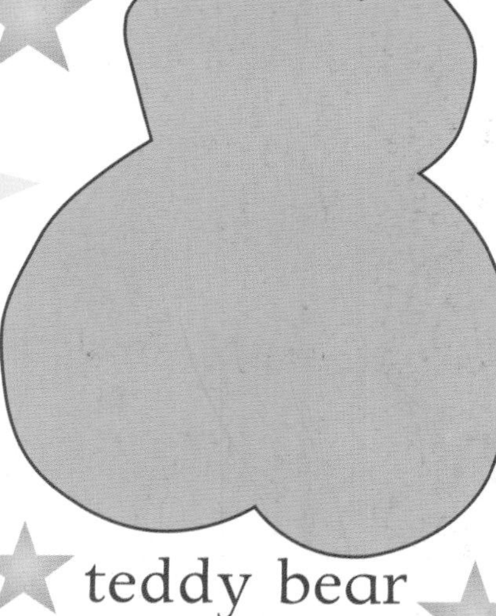

teddy bear

candy

Finally, decorate these pages with sparkly stickers!

Spooky shadows!

Let's find the stickers to complete this page. Can you guess what they are from their shadows?

Can you make up a rhyme about some of these things?